sky blue...

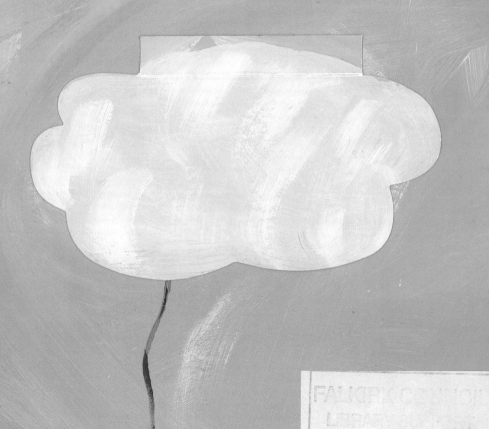

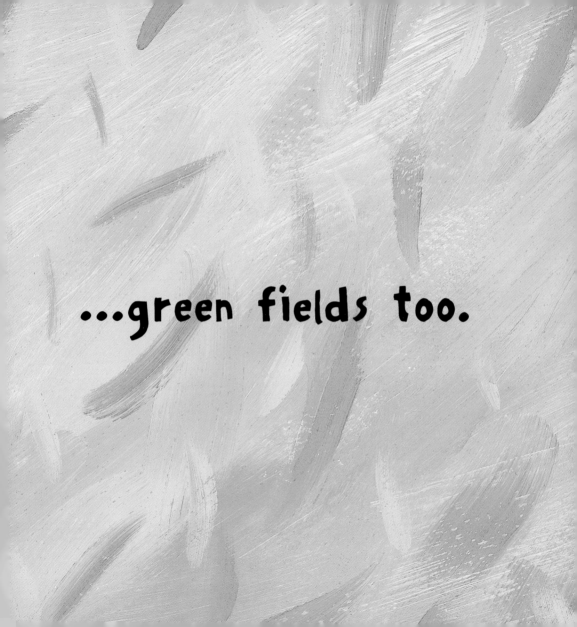

...green fields too.

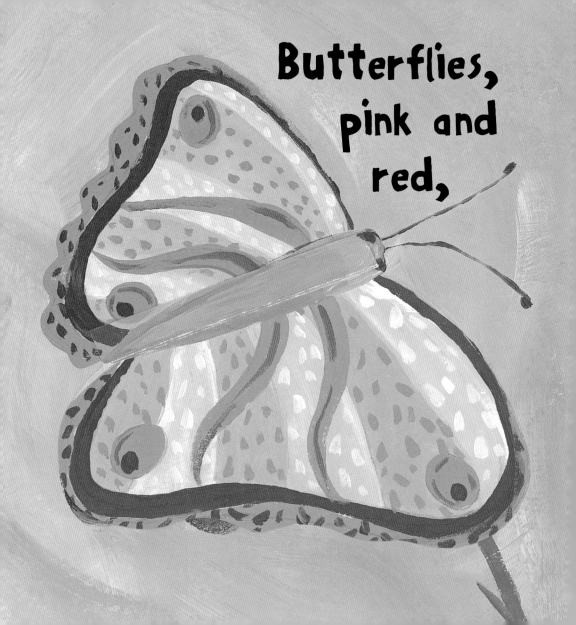

Butterflies,
pink and
red,

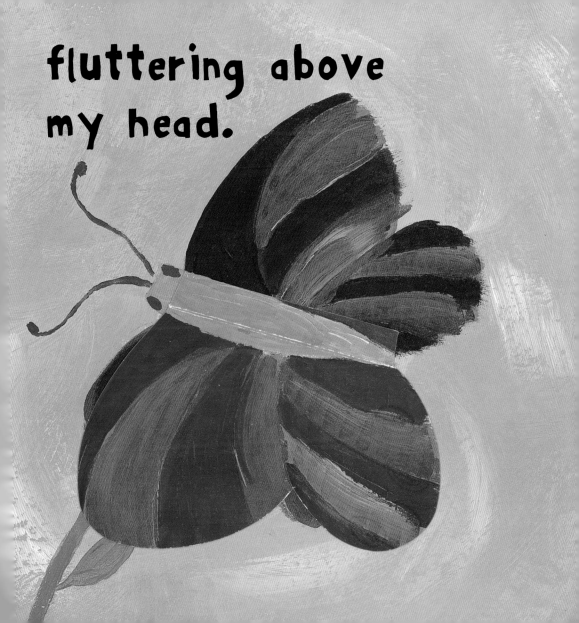

fluttering above
my head.

A soft brown hat

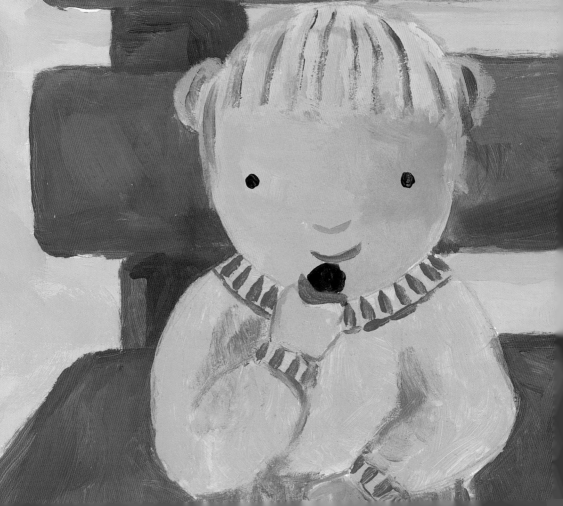

on a wooden seat...

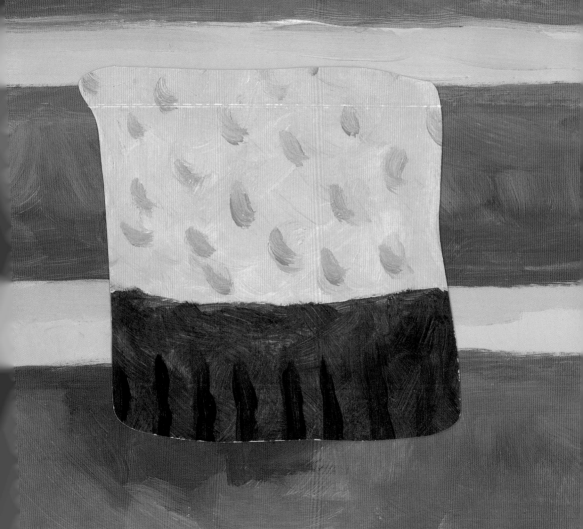

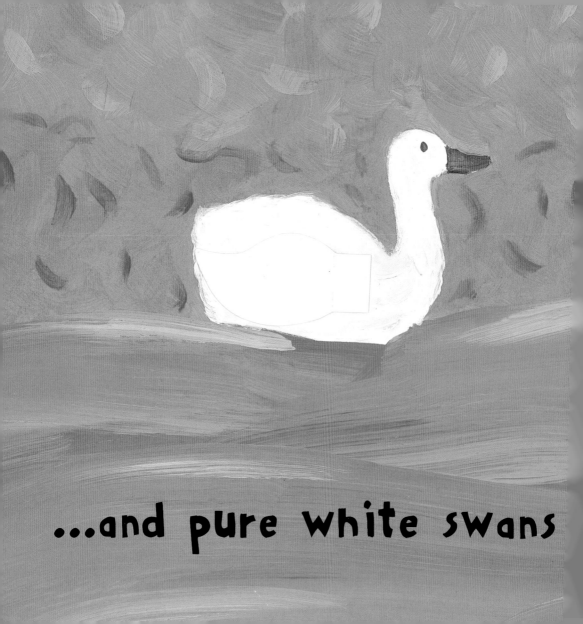

...and pure white swans

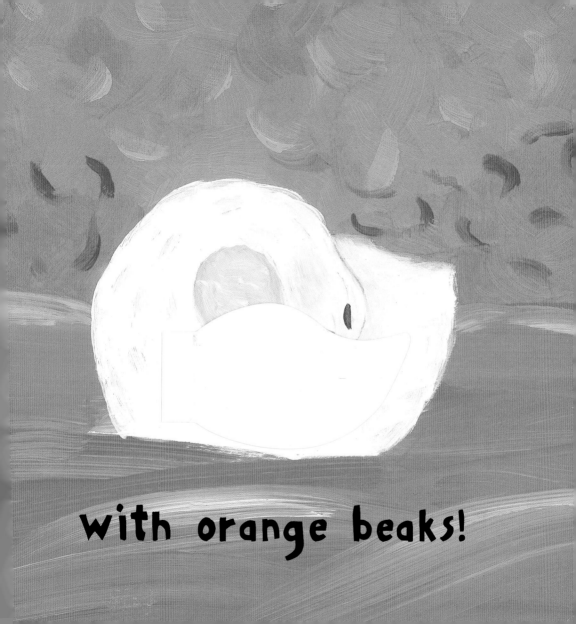

with orange beaks!

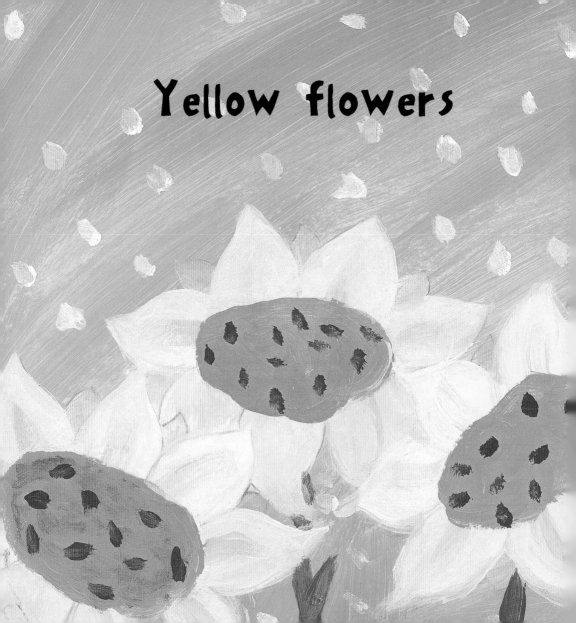

Yellow flowers

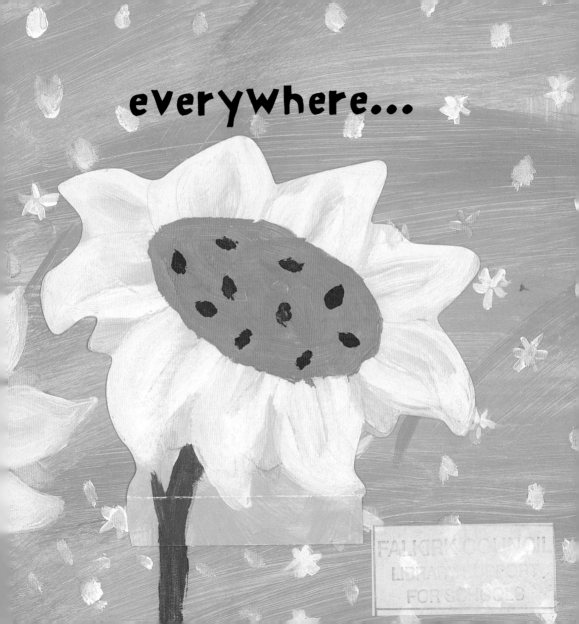

everywhere...

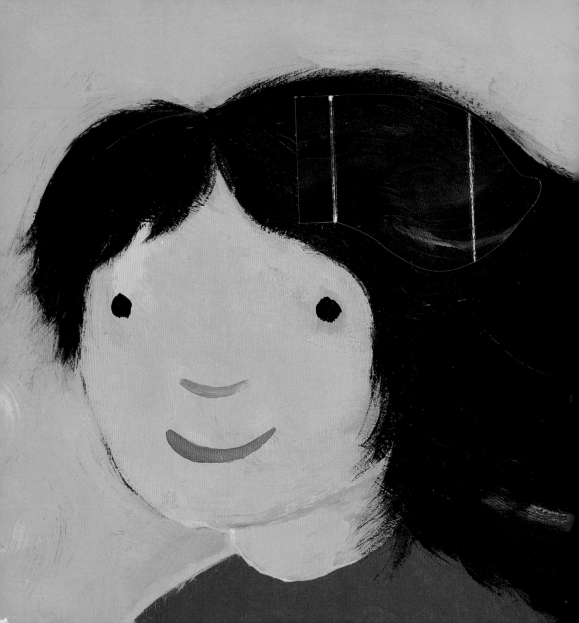